MENTAL MATHS HOMEWORK

FOR 10 YEAR OLDS

SERIES EDITOR
Lin Taylor
The IMPACT Project, University of
North London Enterprises Ltd

AUTHOR
Kate Frood

EDITOR
Joel Lane

EDITORIAL ASSISTANT
David Sandford

SERIES DESIGNER
Anna Oliwa

DESIGNER
Heather C. Sanneh

ILLUSTRATIONS
Mike Miller

COVER ARTWORK
James Alexander/David Oliver
Berkeley Studios

Text © 2000 Kate Frood
© 2000 Scholastic Ltd

Designed using Adobe Pagemaker
Published by Scholastic Ltd, Villiers House, Clarendon
Avenue, Leamington Spa, Warwickshire CV32 5PR

1 2 3 4 5 6 7 8 9 0   0 1 2 3 4 5 6 7 8 9

British Library Cataloguing-in-Publication Data
A catalogue record for this book is available from the
British Library.

ISBN 0-439-01706-8

CONTENTS

IMPACT

ABOUT HOMEWORK

Homework can be a very useful opportunity to practise and develop children's understanding of the work done in school. Games and maths challenges can be very good activities to share with someone at home, especially to develop mental maths strategies and maths language skills. Research* indicates that parental involvement is a major factor in children's educational success. Most parents want to help their children with their school work, but often do not know how and 'traditional' homework does not involve parents. Shared homework activities, such as can be found in *Mental Maths Homework*, are designed to be completed with a parent or helper, such as a sibling, neighbour or other adult who can work with the child. Working one-to-one with an adult in the home environment really has a powerful effect. The National Numeracy Strategy strongly supports this type of homework, which is in line with a variety of government guidelines on the role of parents and making home links.

ABOUT MENTAL MATHS AT HOME

Mental Maths Homework is particularly concerned to develop children's *mental* mathematics. In order to become competent at mental calculation, children need to talk about mathematics and try out different strategies, as well as to practise number facts and skills. Children explaining their mathematics to a parent or helper can help to clarify and develop their understanding of the mathematics. This type of homework, developed by The IMPACT Project, is a *joint* activity: the helper and child working together.

ABOUT MENTAL MATHS HOMEWORK

This series comprises six books, one for each age group from 6–11 years (Year 1/P2–Year 6/P7). Each book contains 36 photocopiable activities – enough for one to be sent home each week throughout the school year, if you wish. The activities concentrate on the number system and developing children's calculation strategies and are designed to fit into your planning, whatever scheme you are using.

Since these books are designed to support the same aims of developing mental maths strategies and vocabulary, they make an ideal follow-on to the class work outlined in Scholastic's other *Mental Maths* series. The objectives for each activity are based on those in the National Numeracy Strategy *Framework for Teaching Mathematics* and the content is appropriate for teachers following other UK curriculum documents.

USING THE ACTIVITIES IN SCHOOL

Although the books are designed for a particular age group they should be used flexibly so that the right level of activity is set for a child or class. All the activities are photocopiable: most are one page, some are two, or require an extra resource page (to be found at the back of the book) for certain games or number card activities. The activities for older children will generally take longer than those for younger children.

BEFORE

It is essential that each activity is introduced to the class before it is sent home with them. This fulfils several crucial functions. It enables the child to explain the activity to the parent or carer; ensuring the child understands the task. It also familiarises the child with the activity; developing motivation and making the activity more accessible. This initial introduction to the activity can be done as part of a regular maths lesson, at the end of the day, or whenever fits in with your class's routine.

AFTER

It is also important that the child brings something back to school from the activity at home. This will not necessarily be substantial, or even anything written, since the activities aim to develop mental mathematics. It is equally important that what the child brings in from home is genuinely valued by you. It is unlikely that parents will be encouraged to share activities with their children if they do not feel that their role is valued either. Each activity indicates what should be brought back to school, and the teachers' notes (on pages 5–8) offer guidance on introducing and working with or reviewing the outcome of each activity.

HELPERS

All the activities have a note to the helper explaining the purpose of the activity and how to help the child, often emphasizing useful vocabulary. The helpers' notes also give indications of how to adapt the activity at home, and what to do if the child gets stuck. Many of the activities are games or fun activities which it is hoped that the parent and child will enjoy doing together and will do again, even when not set for homework, thus increasing the educational benefit. It is particularly beneficial for a game to be played a number of times.

MENTAL MATHS HOMEWORK

OTHER WAYS TO USE THE ACTIVITIES

The activities offered in *Mental Maths Homework* are very flexible and will be used in different ways in different schools. As well as being used for shared homework, they could form the basis of a display or a school challenge, or be used as activities for a maths club. Or, they could be used independently of the school situation by parents who wish to provide stimulating and appropriate educational activities for their children.

USING THE ACTIVITIES AT HOME

If you are a parent using these activities outside of school:

● Choose an activity you both think looks interesting and get going straight away with your child. Make the work *joint:* the helper and the child working out what has to be done *together.*

● Read the instructions to your child and ask him or her to explain what has to be done. It is very effective for the child to do the explaining.

USING HOMEWORK DIARIES

Developing a dialogue between teacher and parent is an important part of shared homework. By working with the child at home, the parent becomes more familiar with the mathematics of the classroom. The teacher also needs to hear from the parent about how the child is faring with the activities. Diaries provide a very good mechanism for this. The helpers and/or the children can comment on the activities (which will give you important feedback) and individual targets can be put into the diary. The diaries can act, therefore, as an important channel of communication. (See below for details about finding out more information about diaries.)

ABOUT THIS BOOK

In *Mental Maths Homework for 10 year olds*, all the activities practise and extend essential numeracy skills as described in the Year 5 objectives of the National Numeracy Strategy *Framework for Teaching Mathematics.* The book includes, for example, activities on knowledge of all the times tables, their multiples and factors, and there is a strong emphasis on choosing and using appropriate number operations and ways of calculating to solve problems.

It is assumed that the children have a good grasp of the key objectives for Year 4, and are now working to extend and consolidate these skills. It is assumed, for example, that they can use known number facts to add or subtract any pair of two-digit numbers mentally, can round integers to the nearest 10 or 100, know the 2, 3, 4, 5 and 10 times tables by heart and can derive the corresponding division facts. The key objectives set out for Year 5 assume that children are working within Level 4 (Primary 3). For some Year 5 pupils, it may be more appropriate to use activities from the *Mental Maths Homework* books for 9 year olds or 11 year olds.

Children involved in the National Numeracy Strategy will be receiving regular mental maths practice in the first part of their daily mathematics lesson. These homework activities provide a range of contexts for extra practice and consolidation, with a particular emphasis on developing the language of mathematics and the application of numeracy skills.

* Bastiani, J. & Wolfendale, S. (1996) *Home-School Work: Review, Reflection and Development* David Fulton Publishers.

THE IMPACT PROJECT

The activities in *Mental Maths Homework* have all been devised by members of The IMPACT Project, based at the University of North London. The project, a pioneer of shared homework with a wealth of experience, is involved in a variety of initiatives concerning parental involvement and homework. It also supports schools in setting up a school framework for shared homework. If you would like help with developing shared homework, planning a whole-school framework for homework or developing mental mathematics at home and at school, maybe through INSET with experienced providers, contact The IMPACT Project. Information about other activities undertaken by the project and about other IMPACT books and resources, such as the IMPACT diaries, is also available from The IMPACT Project.

The IMPACT Project
University of North London
School of Education
166–220 Holloway Road
London
N7 8DB

tel. no. 020 7753 7052

fax. no. 020 7753 5420

e-mail: impact-enquiries@unl.ac.uk
          impact-orders@unl.ac.uk

web: http://www.unl.ac.uk/impact

Underlying all of these activities is the learning objective: Solve mathematical problems or puzzles, recognize and explain patterns and relationships, generalize and predict. Suggest extensions asking 'What if...?'

COUNTING & ORDERING

PRIME TARGET 1

OBJECTIVE: To recognize prime numbers.

BEFORE: The children will need to be familiar with the sequence of prime numbers under 100. When introducing the activity, revise these numbers without drawing attention to the 'pairs'. Encourage the children to look for other similarities between pairs of prime numbers. Is 11 the only prime number below 100 with the same digits? If so, why? Model how to organize the investigation in a systematic way.

AFTER: Share answers. The pairs are: 11 and 11, 13 and 31, 17 and 71, 37 and 73. Share facts about other pairs. Draw up a class chart.

PRIME TARGET 2

OBJECTIVE: To recognize prime numbers.

BEFORE: Do not spend too much time modelling this activity when you introduce it, as the children may spot the answer! Simply ask the question and allow them to express some thoughts. The answer – that two primes can add to make another if one of them is 2 – will soon become apparent if they work methodically.

AFTER: When the homework is returned, encourage the children to explain their answers and to reflect on adding odd and even numbers. Why do they think 2 is a special prime?

BIG COUNT

OBJECTIVE: To add 1, 10, 100 or 1000 to whole numbers.

BEFORE: This game provides a chance to practise mental addition of 1, 10, 100 and 1000. Play it a few times in class, recording the moves on the board, so that the children understand the rules clearly. Emphasize the need to say the total carefully after each new addition. Demonstrate how to gain the loser's 'bonus' by stating how much has been added in total.

AFTER: Play the game again, with the children in pairs. Encourage them to work as fast as they can.

ROUNDABOUT BINGO

OBJECTIVE: To round whole numbers to the nearest 10 or 100.

BEFORE: The children will need to be familiar with the idea of 'rounding'. Demonstrate the activity in class before sending it home, and play a game with the class so that they understand the rules. Challenge them to play with four numbers for which the same hundred is the nearest (for example: 278, 299, 323, 345). Does this reduce their chance of winning?

AFTER: Use rounding as an oral and mental starter.

GOOD NEIGHBOURS

OBJECTIVE: To recognize and extend number sequences.

BEFORE: The children will need to be familiar with the term 'consecutive'. Introduce this activity by asking for sequences of numbers that are consecutive. Then ask whether anyone can make 9 from consecutive numbers. What about 18? Introduce the investigation as a challenge. Remind the class to work in a systematic and ordered way.

AFTER: When the results are brought back, look at the groupings of 'good neighbour' numbers which can be made from two consecutive numbers, three consecutive numbers, and so on.

EITHER SIDE OF ZERO

OBJECTIVE: To count on or back in small steps, extending beyond zero when counting back.

BEFORE: Introduce this activity by doing some quickfire calculations such as 7 + 6 and 5 – 3. Then introduce calculations that produce negative answers, such as 5 – 9. Play a game against a class member, so that the children are sure of the rules. Try to get the class thinking: *Is there a first card to turn over that guarantees a win?* Encourage the children to do the mental calculations as fast as they can.

AFTER: Work on more complex calculations (with bigger numbers or more than one step) that generate negative numbers.

I'VE GOT A NUMBER

OBJECTIVE: To recognize properties of numbers.

BEFORE: This is an excellent game for oral and mental work, and really sharpens children's ability to ask and use questions in maths. Demonstrate how to refine the questions as the field of possible answers narrows. Use a 100 square, or write possible numbers or number ranges on the board. Demonstrate both useful and pointless questions. Play the game in class a few times.

AFTER: Play the game in class again after the children have tried it at home. Check whether their questioning skills have improved.

ADDITION & SUBTRACTION

SQUARE UP TO 100

OBJECTIVES: To use known number facts and place value for mental addition. To estimate by approximating, then check the result.

BEFORE: This is an excellent way of practising two-digit addition, using place value and estimation.

Demonstrate the example clearly. Draw the children's attention to which digit is tens and which is units in each number. Model adding up the four numbers. Lead the children to an understanding that the total in the units column needs to end in 0.

AFTER: Share solutions. One solution is:

$$1 \quad 5$$
$$1 \quad 7 \quad \rightarrow 15 + 17 + 11 + 57 = 100$$

The children can make up similar puzzles in pairs and swap them with other pairs around the class.

MONEY SORT

OBJECTIVE: To develop and refine the use of informal writing with mental methods for addition.

BEFORE: The children will need to be clear about how to tackle this kind of problem before taking it home. Devise a similar problem and solve it as a class, sharing different methods that could be used. Revise strategies for mental addition.

AFTER: Share the solution. Max and Rachel have £1.06 each: 71p, 12p, 17p, 6p and 11p, 32p, 17p, 46p.

9S NETBALL

OBJECTIVE: To add or subtract the nearest multiple of 10, then adjust.

BEFORE: Introduce the strategy for adding 9, 19, and so on in class before handing this out. Motivate the class to practise at home by setting up a class knockout tournament for the following week.

AFTER: Carry out the tournament.

TAKE SIX DIGITS

OBJECTIVE: To develop and refine written methods for addition, building on mental methods.

BEFORE: This task is very open-ended. The children need to be aware of all the possible ways of generating answers (by using different numbers of + signs and varying their positions), and the many extra answers that are possible if decimals are used. Introduce the challenge by asking the class whether anyone can make a selected target total (perhaps 135 or 189) following the rules given. Then ask what the lowest possible total is, and the highest.

AFTER: Draw up a master chart of all the different answers the children have generated.

UNFAIR SHARE

OBJECTIVE: To develop and refine written methods for addition, building on mental methods.

BEFORE: This follows on nicely from 'Money sort' on page 17. Remind the children of the successful method they used for that task. How would they adapt it for this challenge?

AFTER: Share answers. The helper should have 200 and the child 100; several combinations are possible.

SUM DIGITS

OBJECTIVE: To use known number facts and place value to add.

BEFORE: Introduce this by generating one possible solution to the first problem together, so that the method is clearly modelled. Take extra care to explain that some digits in the answer could have two possible meanings: a 4 could be 4 alone or the units digit of 14. Model how 'carrying' will affect the solution. Challenge the children to find other solutions. Explain the extra rule in the second problem carefully.

AFTER: Go through all of the solutions found. An example for the second problem is 715 + 248 = 963.

CRYPTARITHMS

OBJECTIVE: Use known number facts and place value to add.

BEFORE: This activity follows on from 'Sum digits' on page 18. Revise with the children what they learned in that activity. Work through a sample cryptarithm – for example:

M A K E	8 9 5 7
+ S A F E	+ 4 9 6 7
P L A N S	1 3 9 2 4

Start by telling them that S = 4. So what could E be? This highlights the fact that a 4 could be 4 alone or the units digit of 14.

AFTER: Share answers. One solution is: 429 + 7430 = 7859. The only solution to the 'Bet you can't' challenge is: 91 + 10 = 101.

ALPHABETICAL ARITHMETIC

OBJECTIVES: To use known number facts and place value to add. To add several numbers.

BEFORE: This is a highly motivating way to practise addition and use logic to solve a problem. In class, solve the vegetable word problem together (the answer is beetroot). Ask who thinks his or her name will have a high value. Why? Ask everyone to try out his or her own name to practise the method.

AFTER: When the answers come in, compile a grand class list of words that total 100. Extend the challenge to the whole school through newsletters and assemblies! The other answers to the problem on the sheet are: excellent, printer, hospital, wizards.

STEP UP

OBJECTIVE: Use known number facts and place value to add.

BEFORE: The children will need to be familiar with the 'pyramid' type of addition and subtraction problem. This version involves missing base numbers. Work through a different example with the class before sending it home, so the children understand exactly how the method works. Guide the children into making reasonable guesses, and encourage them to find a method of working out the missing numbers other than trial and error.

AFTER: Share answers. The missing base numbers are 12 and 7. The rule to find them should be similar to: 'Take both side numbers away from the number above – the result is twice the missing base number.'

MULTIPLICATION & DIVISION

FROM 5S TO 50S

OBJECTIVE: To multiply whole numbers by 10.
BEFORE: You will need to have taught the process of multiplying by 10 to the children, so that they are clear about the digit-shifting principle. Warn the class that there will be a 50 times table test next week.
AFTER: Carry out the test.

SECRET NUMBERS

OBJECTIVE: To understand the operation of multiplication and the associated vocabulary.
BEFORE: This could be used as an oral and mental starter, so that the children fully understand the steps. Emphasize the words **sum** and **product**. Encourage the children to note down possible pairs of numbers after each clue – remembering that in this case, 3 + 2 is different from 2 + 3. Model how to eliminate possibilities after each step.
AFTER: Play this again as an oral and mental starter. Introduce mystery numbers over 10 or less than 1.

MAKING MULTIPLES

OBJECTIVES: To know multiplication facts by heart. To recognize multiples of numbers to 10.
BEFORE: Play a demonstration game before sending this activity home. Talk carefully through each move as you play. Encourage the children to spot possible answers. If time allows, let them play in small groups.
AFTER: The children play again in pairs.

PRODUCT PONTOON

OBJECTIVES: To know multiplication facts by heart. To recognize multiples.
BEFORE: Introduce this game by choosing a small group to play it with you in class. Once you have played a game, work out the highest and the lowest possible scores with the class. Set some problems, such as: *If your first card is a 9 and your opponent has a 2, what second cards might you both get that would cause your opponent to win?*
AFTER: The children play again in groups of three. Introduce the 'third card' rule to groups if possible.

FACTOR GRID

OBJECTIVE: To identify factors.
BEFORE: This game needs careful explanation. Start with some fast oral and mental work on factors. Play the game against a child to demonstrate the rules. The children should then play the game in pairs, so that they are really sure of how to play.
AFTER: Go through the completed gameboards. Can the children devise a new gameboard which would score 18 (the maximum score) if 6, 6, 5, 5, 4, 4, 3, 3 and 2 were rolled?

SORT THE SWEETS

OBJECTIVES: To recognize multiples. To know some tests for divisibility.
BEFORE: The children will need to be familiar with patterns of divisibility. Work through a prepared example that is similar in logic, and encourage the children to work out facts about the mystery number from clues – for example, 'If the number can be shared exactly into piles of 10, it must end in 0.'
AFTER: Share the answer, 76. Encourage discussion of the task and how the children reached their answers.

GET SET, GO!

OBJECTIVES: To recognize multiples. To identify factors.
BEFORE: Start with some oral and mental work on multiples. Draw a large Venn diagram on the board and demonstrate the game.
AFTER: Go through the answers. Ask children to explain how they worked. Emphasize the patterns of divisibility.

PERSISTENT NUMBERS

OBJECTIVE: To know multiplication facts by heart.
BEFORE: Explain clearly what is meant by the 'persistence' of a number. Demonstrate the procedure and set the challenge. Emphasize the need to work systematically.
AFTER: Share results and draw up a class chart. The smallest number with a persistence of 2 is 25; the smallest number with a persistence of 3 is 39. Ask: *Can anyone explain why this is?* (25 is the smallest number to have a digit product over 9. 3 and 9 are the smallest numbers to have a digit product over 25.)

MYSTERY SYMBOLS

OBJECTIVES: To use known facts. To use doubling and halving.
BEFORE: Draw a similar puzzle on the board and work through it with the class, inviting the children to make and explain guesses. Model how to look for a good place to start, and how you can make and test assumptions: *Let's say diamond is... so clubs will be....*
AFTER: Share answers, then let pairs of children devise mystery grids for each other. (The solution is: diamond = 4, club = 6, heart = 3.)

MYSTERY SQUARES

OBJECTIVES: To know factors. To use known facts.
BEFORE: Draw up a standard (10 × 10) addition grid, and complete it quickly as a whole-class activity. Now look at an addition grid with all the answers, but none of the outer numbers. Can the class work it out? Introduce the homework, which has the added difficulty that some answers are missing. Stress that they can use the numbers 1–10 once only.
AFTER: Share solutions. Prepare some more difficult grids for follow-up work in class. There is an example in *Mental Maths Homework for 11 year olds* (page 33).

MULTISTEP & MIXED OPERATIONS

BUTTONS IN A JAR

OBJECTIVE: To choose and use appropriate number operations to solve problems.

BEFORE: Set the problem, then work through a prepared similar example to demonstrate the logic. Focus on the language of the question, and make sure the children understand which operations are necessary.

AFTER: Share the answer. There are 6 green buttons, 12 white, 5 blue and 13 red. Show the class how algebra can be used to solve the problem rather than trial and improvement.

3-WAY BINGO

OBJECTIVE: To use known number facts to add, subtract and multiply mentally.

BEFORE: Ask the children to play the game in pairs. Work through the dice throws needed to make each number on the board as a quickfire mental exercise. Discuss which numbers will be harder and easier to cover.

AFTER: With the class, make up a more sophisticated Bingo game based on multiplication and division facts.

DOUBLE-AGE PAIRS

OBJECTIVE: To use doubling and halving to solve a problem.

BEFORE: Pose the questions to the class to get them thinking. See whether anyone has a sibling currently twice or half his or her age. Ask: *Will this still be true after you have both had your next birthday?* Ask whether anyone in the class was ever twice as old (in years) as a friend in the class.

AFTER: Take time to go through the answers. With the class, devise a way of collating the data.

MYSTERY NUMBER SEARCH 1

OBJECTIVE: To know squares of numbers to 10 × 10.

BEFORE: Make sure the children understand how to find square numbers. Read the question very slowly and break it into steps. Try some sample numbers to show the method that is required.

AFTER: Share the answer, 48. Ask: *How long did it take you to find this?*

MYSTERY NUMBER SEARCH 2

OBJECTIVE: To use doubling and addition to solve a word problem.

BEFORE: This problem is a bit of a tongue-twister! Read it out very slowly, breaking it into stages and modelling each stage on the board (as shown on the activity sheet). Remind the children of the need to be systematic and organized.

AFTER: Share the answer, 25.

MONEY PROBLEM

OBJECTIVE: To use all four operations to solve a word problem involving money.

BEFORE: Read through the question in class. Discuss reasonable guesses. Try out an incorrect guess that you have prepared, to model the method of enquiry.

AFTER: Share the solution – twelve 10ps, five 5ps and five 1ps. Ask some children to show you how they worked it out. If possible, display all their working.

NUMBER CRUNCH

OBJECTIVE: To choose and use appropriate number operations to solve problems.

BEFORE: Explain the game in class and play it together, with the children working in pairs. Set a time limit, then share all the answers found.

AFTER: Make a class chart showing the answers found and the number sentences used to make them.

HOW MANY 5S?

OBJECTIVE: To use all four operations to solve word problems involving numbers based on 'real life'.

BEFORE: Read out the question in class. Allow free discussion, initially with a partner, so that estimates and strategies can be discussed. Take some estimates and record them. Now help the children to see patterns in the counting up, and lead them to see possible quick ways: 1–10 will be 11 digits; 11–20 will be 20 digits, and so will 21–30 and so on. Ask: *Can anyone see a quick way of calculating how many 5s are needed?* Remind the children to watch out for 5s in the tens digits as well.

AFTER: Share answers and strategies. The book has 221 pages; 5 is used 42 times.

KEEP FIT CALCULATIONS

OBJECTIVE: To use the relationship between multiplication and addition to solve a problem.

BEFORE: Devise a similar problem and work through possible ways of solving it. Take estimates from children and ask them to explain their reasoning. Stress the need to be methodical and systematic.

AFTER: Share the solution, 8 circuits. Compare the strategies used. Model how algebra can be used to solve the problem. Invite children who have made up their own problems to challenge the class.

MOUTH-WATERING MATHS

OBJECTIVE: To use all four operations to solve word problems involving measures.

BEFORE: Explain the task, and demonstrate using a recipe of your own. Ask the children to help you find half of, and ten times, each amount.

AFTER: Ask the children to write the shopping list they would need for their 'ten times' recipes.

PRIME TARGET 1

YOU WILL NEED: a helper, a pencil and paper.

YOU ARE GOING TO: investigate 'twin primes'.
❑ Here is a challenge for you and your helper:

How many 2-digit prime numbers can you find that are STILL prime numbers when their digits are reversed?

Here's an example: 17 (and 71).

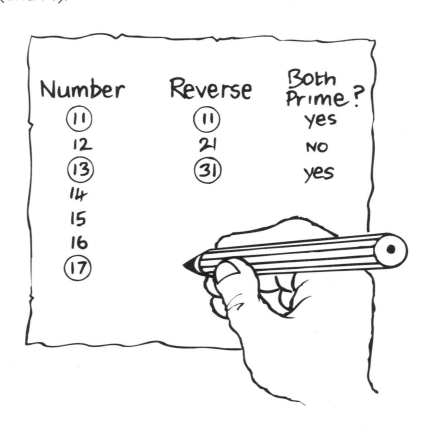

BET YOU CAN'T
Find similar pairs of 3-digit prime numbers.

DEAR HELPER

THE POINT OF THIS ACTIVITY: is to familiarize your child with the idea of prime numbers and the set of prime numbers below 100. A **prime number** is a number that has only two **factors** (numbers that will divide into it exactly): itself and 1. Prime numbers are an important group of numbers to recognize and understand.

Show your child how to be systematic and organized. Start with 11 and work upwards, drawing a chart like the one shown above.

YOU MIGHT LIKE TO: ask your child to find a link between each number and its reverse. For example,

with 12 and 21: neither is prime, but both are in the 3 times table. This is also true of 15 and 51. Your child can write down any links that he or she finds on another chart like the one shown above.

IF YOU GET STUCK: Help your child to find all the prime numbers under 20, using counters or cubes. Which numbers will share into 2 or 3 equal piles, and which will not? Practise reciting the sequence of prime numbers to 20.

Please sign: . . . .

PRIME TARGET 2

COUNTING AND ORDERING

YOU WILL NEED: a helper, a pencil and paper.

YOU ARE GOING TO: find out more about prime numbers.
❑ With your helper, investigate this question:

Which two prime numbers add up to another prime number?

❑ Find as many pairs of prime numbers that add up to a prime number as you can. Use this list of all the prime numbers under 100 to help you:

2 3 5 7 11 13 17 19 23 29 31 37 41 43 47 59 61 67 71 73 79 83 89 97

❑ Discuss your findings with your helper. Write a list of all the pairs you found, and anything that you have noticed about them.
❑ Bring your answers and comments back to school.

BET YOU CAN'T
Find **three** prime numbers that add up to a prime number.

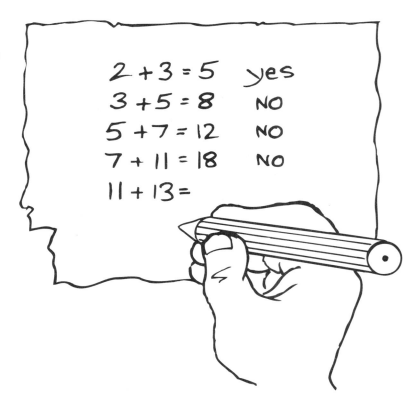

2 + 3 = 5   yes
3 + 5 = 8   NO
5 + 7 = 12   NO
7 + 11 = 18 NO
11 + 13 =

IMPACT

DEAR HELPER

THE POINT OF THIS ACTIVITY: is to familiarize your child with the idea of prime numbers and the set of prime numbers below 100. A **prime number** is a number that has only two **factors** (numbers that will divide into it exactly): itself and 1. Prime numbers are an important group of numbers to recognize and understand.

Start by adding the smaller prime numbers together. Your child should soon see a pattern emerging which will make the search for answers easier.

YOU MIGHT LIKE TO: help your child learn the set of prime numbers under 100 by heart.

IF YOU GET STUCK: show your child how to be systematic and organized. Start with 2 and add each of the other prime numbers in turn: 2 + 2, 2 + 3, 2 + 5 and so on. Then start with 3: 3 + 3, 3 + 5, 3 + 7 and so on. Write out your results as a chart.

Please sign: . . . .

BIG COUNT

YOU WILL NEED: a helper, a pencil and paper.

YOU ARE GOING TO: play a place value game.
- ❑ Agree with your helper on a four-digit start number – for example, 4876.
- ❑ Now take turns to add **one** of these:

     1
     10
     100
or   1000
- ❑ After each addition, say the new number out loud.
- ❑ The player who finally says a new number in which **all four digits are the same** scores a point.

For example:

You	4876	+1	= 4877
Your helper	4877	+1	= 4878
You	4878	+10	= 4888
Your helper	4888	+1000	= 5888
You	5888	+1000	= 6888
Your helper	6888	+1000	= 7888
You	7888	+1000	= 8888 **The winner!**

❑ The loser now has a chance to score a point by saying how much was added to the start number to reach the winning number. In this example, the total amount added was 1000 + 1000 + 1000 + 1000 + 10 + 1 + 1 = **4012**.

❑ Play the game several times. Who scores more points? Keep a written record of each game.
❑ Bring your records back to school.

YOU MIGHT LIKE TO TRY
Finding out which start numbers make the game hardest.

DEAR HELPER

THE POINT OF THIS ACTIVITY: is to help your child to add and subtract 1, 10, 100 or 1000 in his or her head. This is an important skill in mental calculation. The trick is to use place value and simply add 1 to the appropriate column.

Warm up by simply taking turns to add 1 to a large number. Then take turns to add 10, then 100 and finally 1000. Do each addition enough times to make your child notice the language rhythms of the number sequence.

YOU MIGHT LIKE TO: allow subtraction in the game too – with the rule that you cannot subtract the same amount that has just been added on.

IF YOU GET STUCK: write each new number down on a piece of paper, in columns labelled **Th H T U**, as you say it. This will help your child to see what effects different possible additions will have.

Please sign: . . . .

NAME DATE

ROUNDABOUT BINGO

YOU WILL NEED: one or more helpers, a dice, a pencil and paper for each player, counters.

YOU ARE GOING TO: practise rounding numbers.

- ❑ Each player chooses four numbers between 50 and 649 and writes them in four circles on his or her piece of paper.
- ❑ Roll the dice. The number rolled is a number of hundreds – so a 4 means 400.
- ❑ If you have a number for which this is the **nearest hundred**, you can cover it with a counter. You can only cover one number per go.

  Note: To find the nearest hundred to a number ending in 50, **round up** (for example, 350 rounds to 400).
- ❑ The first person to cover all four of his or her numbers shouts 'BINGO!' and is the winner.

- ❑ Bring your numbers back to school for a whole-class game.

BET YOU CAN'T

Play a version where numbers between 5 and 64 are chosen, and the number rolled on the dice gives the nearest ten.

DEAR HELPER

THE POINT OF THIS ACTIVITY: is to improve your child's skills in rounding to the nearest hundred or ten. Rounding is an important skill in finding rough answers through estimation: '367 × 79 is about 400 × 80 = 32 000'. It can also be useful for mental addition and subtraction:
'48 + 39 = (48 + 2) + (39 – 2) = 50 + 37 = 87'.

Ask questions such as *What number are you hoping we'll roll next?* as you play, to help your child think ahead and predict. Reinforce the mathematical rule that you **round up** from 50 to the nearest hundred (or from 5 to the nearest ten).

YOU MIGHT LIKE TO:
- Think about whether there are any 'best' numbers to choose, or whether the game just depends on chance.
- Extend the game by choosing numbers from 0–100. Make cards for the multiples of 10 from 10–100. Turn these over instead of rolling the dice, and round the chosen numbers to the nearest ten.

IF YOU GET STUCK: draw a number line to help your child see the nearest ten or hundred to any number.

Please sign: . . . .

GOOD NEIGHBOURS

YOU WILL NEED: a helper, pencil and paper.

YOU ARE GOING TO: investigate some properties of numbers.
Good neighbour numbers are numbers which can be made by adding
consecutive (next-door neighbour) numbers together.

For example:
3 + 4 = 7
5 + 6 + 7 = 18
11 + 12 = 23
21 + 22 + 23 + 24 = 90
so 7, 18, 23 and 90 are good neighbour numbers.
But some numbers are **not** good neighbours.

❑ How many good and bad neighbours can you find, working with your helper?
You will need to be well-organized and work in a **systematic** way.
❑ You may use two, three or more consecutive numbers to make a good
neighbour number.
❑ Draw up a chart and write
in your answers. Bring the chart
back to school.

Number	Can it be made ?
1	0 + 1
2	?
3	1 + 2
4	?
5	2 + 3
6	1 + 2 + 3
7	

BET YOU CAN'T
Find a pattern in the bad neighbour numbers.

DEAR HELPER

THE POINT OF THIS ACTIVITY: is to develop your
child's ability to approach a problem in a logical and
systematic way. It will also familiarize him or her with the
idea of **consecutive** numbers (numbers which follow in
a sequence, with no gaps). This idea is important for
looking at number sequences. For example: 2, 4, 6, 8
and 10 are the first five consecutive even numbers.
   Start by trying to make 1, then 2 and so on. Leave
any numbers that you cannot make and return to
them later.

YOU MIGHT LIKE TO: ask your child to divide the good
neighbour numbers into groups – those that can be made
with two consecutive numbers, then three, four and so on.
Is there a pattern?

IF YOU GET STUCK: just investigate numbers that can be
made with pairs of consecutive numbers: 3 + 4, 4 + 5, 5 + 6
and so on. Is there a pattern?

Please sign: . . . .

COUNTING AND ORDERING

IMPACT

COUNTING AND ORDERING

EITHER SIDE OF ZERO

YOU WILL NEED: a helper, a pencil and paper, the cards in one suit (Ace to 10) from a pack.

YOU ARE GOING TO: play a game involving positive and negative numbers.

❑ Shuffle the cards and put them face down in a pile. Decide which player is 'positive' and which player is 'negative'.

❑ Start at zero. Take turns to turn over a card and add or subtract that number according to whose turn it is. Keep a note of the running total.

❑ When there are no cards left, a point goes to the player on whose side of zero the running total has ended up.

Here is a sample game:
You are 'positive' (adding). Your helper is 'negative' (subtracting).

You turn over 8	$0 + 8 = 8$
Your helper turns over 2	$8 - 2 = 6$
You turn over 3	$6 + 3 = 9$
Your helper turns over 7	$9 - 7 = 2$
You turn over Ace	$2 + 1 = 3$
Your helper turns over 5	$3 - 5 = -2$
You turn over 4	$-2 + 4 = 2$
Your helper turns over 9	$2 - 9 = -7$
You turn over 10	$-7 + 10 = 3$
Your helper turns over 6	$3 - 6 = -3$

Your helper wins because the final answer is negative.

❑ Be ready to add and subtract across zero in a quick-fire test when you return to school!

YOU MIGHT LIKE TO TRY

Playing with two sets of 1–10 cards: turn over two cards at a time and create a two-digit number to add or subtract.

DEAR HELPER

THE POINT OF THIS ACTIVITY: is to help your child become familiar with negative numbers and be able to do simple addition and subtraction moving across zero. The context of a game makes the idea of negative numbers easier to deal with.

Play several times, taking turns to add or subtract. Take opportunities to describe negative numbers in real contexts – for example, when watching the weather forecast together.

YOU MIGHT LIKE TO: investigate whether who goes first makes a difference to who wins.

IF YOU GET STUCK: draw a number line from –10 to +10 and demonstrate how the running total in the game moves above and below zero.

Please sign: . . . .

IMPACT

I'VE GOT A NUMBER

YOU WILL NEED: a helper, a pencil and paper.

YOU ARE GOING TO: find mystery numbers by asking questions.

❏ Play against your helper, taking turns to choose a number under 100 and write it secretly on a piece of paper.

❏ When it's your turn, put the piece of paper in your pocket. Your helper must ask you questions to try to work out what your secret number is.

❏ The questions asked must have the answer **Yes** or **No**. Your helper should write down each question and its answer to gather clues.

Here are some good questions to ask:
'Is it greater than...?'
'Is it less than...?'
'Is it between....?'
'Is it odd?'
'Is it a multiple of...?'
'Do the digits add up to more than...?'
'Do the digits add up to...?'
'Is it a prime number?'
'Is it a square number?'

❏ Can you guess each other's numbers with fewer than ten questions?
❏ Bring some good questions back to school, ready for a whole-class game.

BET YOU CAN'T
Include decimal numbers and numbers below zero.

DEAR HELPER

THE POINT OF THIS ACTIVITY: is to help your child learn how to ask and answer questions – a key skill in maths. It also brings together what your child has learned about numbers and how to describe them.

As your child asks questions, point out any question that is unnecessary – for example, 'Is it under 50?' (*No*) should not be followed with 'Is it under 30?', since the first question has established that it is not. If you know that a number is odd, there is no point in asking 'Is it a multiple of 2?'

YOU MIGHT LIKE TO: choose a number over 100. The questions will then have to be more precise!

IF YOU GET STUCK: start with a number below 20. When you have found some good questions to ask, try a number up to 50 – and then, if you like, try a number up to 100.

Please sign: . . . .

SQUARE UP TO 100

YOU WILL NEED: a helper, a pencil and paper.

YOU ARE GOING TO: solve an addition puzzle.

❑ Can you arrange four digits from 1–9 (a digit may be used more than once) in four boxes so that when you add the two 2-digit numbers reading across and the two 2-digit numbers reading down, the total is 100?

For example:

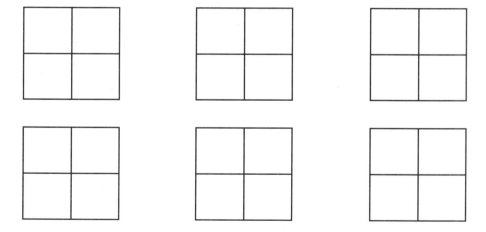

$$
\begin{array}{r}
32 \\
41 \\
34 \\
+\,21 \\
\hline
128
\end{array}
$$
Too high.

❑ Bring your solution, and any other puzzles you have made up, back to school.

YOU MIGHT LIKE TO TRY

Making up some similar puzzles to try on the class, using these squares.

DEAR HELPER

THE POINT OF THIS ACTIVITY: is to encourage your child to practise adding a series of 2-digit numbers mentally or on paper. It also requires your child to use estimation skills and think carefully about what digits to choose and where to place them.

YOU MIGHT LIKE TO: make up some puzzles of your own. Write four random digits in a grid, and add up the four 2-digit numbers you have made to find your target number. Hide the grid and show your child the total. He

or she can present you with a similar puzzle, and you can race to solve each other's!

IF YOU GET STUCK: tell your child that the top left-hand square should hold quite a low digit, as it will form the tens digit in two numbers. The bottom right-hand square will form the units digit in two numbers.

Please sign: . . . .

ADDITION AND SUBTRACTION

IMPACT

MONEY SORT

YOU WILL NEED: a helper, a pencil and paper.

YOU ARE GOING TO: solve a money puzzle.

Max and Rachel are given eight bags of small change to share equally between them. They have to keep the money in the bags, but they do not have to take four bags each.

 71p
 11p
 32p
 6p

 17p
 12p
 17p
 46p

❏ They can't work out how to do it fairly. Can you help them?

❏ Bring your solution back to school.

BET YOU CAN'T

Solve this problem. **If all the money were tipped out into one big pile, and their little brother Peter wanted a fair share as well, how much would have to be added to the money pile for them all to have a fair share?**

DEAR HELPER

THE POINT OF THIS ACTIVITY: is to practise addition skills, and to solve a problem by making sensible guesses and checking them. Encourage your child to add up the numbers in his or her head. Talk through the addition calculation, using strategies such as: adding the tens first and then the units; starting with the largest number.

YOU MIGHT LIKE TO: make up a similar problem

together for your child to take back to school.

IF YOU GET STUCK:
● Add up all the bags of money to find the grand total, then try to find out which bags equal half that amount.
● Use practical materials to help – for example, dried beans in cups to represent each bag.

Please sign: . . . .

ADDITION AND SUBTRACTION

IMPACT

9S NETBALL

YOU WILL NEED: a helper, a pencil and paper.

YOU ARE GOING TO: practise adding 9 in your head.
❏ Ask your helper to 'throw' a number under 100 at you – for example, 17.
❏ You must add 9 and then 'throw' it back as fast as you can: 26.
❏ Your helper must add 9 to the new number and 'throw' it back: 35.
❏ Keep the rally going by 'throwing' numbers in this way until one of you makes a mistake.
❏ Now try again, but this time **subtracting** 9.
❏ Bring a record of your longest rally back to school.

> **HANDY HINT!**
> A good way to add 9 in your head is to add 10 and take away 1. A good way to subtract 9 in your head is to take away 10 and add 1.

YOU MIGHT LIKE TO TRY
❏ Making the game harder by choosing start numbers over 100.
❏ Playing the same game, but this time adding 19, or 29, or 59, or 199, or 499... any number that ends in a 9!

DEAR HELPER

THE POINT OF THIS ACTIVITY: is to teach your child a useful mental calculation strategy for adding or subtracting numbers that end in a 9. The strategy is: *Use the nearest multiple of 10, then adjust by 1.* Children are encouraged to use this method in school, and this activity helps them to do it quickly. Begin with simple start numbers and progress according to how well your child responds.

YOU MIGHT LIKE TO: agree on both a start number and a target number (such as 32 and 130 respectively). Whoever takes the running total over the target number wins. Can your child predict who will win from the start?

IF YOU GET STUCK: use paper and pencil to illustrate the process of adding 10 and then subtracting 1. For example:
16 + 10 = 26
26 − 1 = 25
so 16 + 9 = 25

Please sign: . . . .

TAKE SIX DIGITS

YOU WILL NEED: a helper, a pencil and paper.

YOU ARE GOING TO: work on an addition problem.
❑ Look at these six digits:

1 2 4 5 7 8

❑ How many different answers can you and your helper make by putting them into different numbers and adding the numbers?
❑ You must follow these rules:
• You cannot change the order of the digits.
• You may only use addition.
• You may not use a calculator, but you may use paper and a pencil.
• An answer using decimals counts as two answers!

For example, you could make:
    12 + 45 + 78 = 135   1 + 245 + 7 + 8 = 261   12.4 + 57.8 = 70.2

❑ Bring your list of answers back to school, including the lowest and highest totals you made.

BET YOU CAN'T
See how many answers you can make using subtraction, following the same rules.

DEAR HELPER

THE POINT OF THIS ACTIVITY: is to practise addition, as well as reading and understanding large numbers. It also develops problem-solving skills and creative thinking about numbers.

Start by looking at the digits with your child: work out how to create the largest possible answer, and then the smallest. Work together, sharing answers as you go along. You may find it helpful to work systematically: start by using only one + sign in different places, then two + signs and so on.

YOU MIGHT LIKE TO: give your child this challenge.

You may use only one addition sign, but you may put the six digits in any order. What is the highest answer you can make?

IF YOU GET STUCK:
● Limit yourselves to the target of making 10 different answers.
● Use a calculator so that your child does not get bogged down with the calculations, and is free to think creatively about placing the + signs.

Please sign: . . . .

ADDITION AND SUBTRACTION

IMPACT

UNFAIR SHARE

YOU WILL NEED: a helper, a pencil and paper.

YOU ARE GOING TO: try to solve a difficult sharing problem.

❏ Can you and your helper share these numbers between you so that your helper has a total **twice as large** as yours? (You cannot split up any of the numbers.)

34 21 28 55 19
32 26 23 45 17

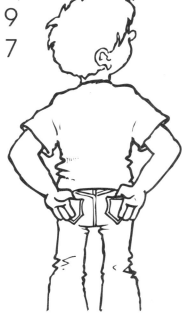

❏ Bring your solution, and any problems you have made up, back to school with you.

BET YOU CAN'T
Make up your own version of this problem, using different numbers.

DEAR HELPER

THE POINT OF THIS ACTIVITY: is to practise addition and subtraction skills, and to use logical thinking in order to solve a problem. Finding the answer requires some persistence, but the best way to start is to add up the grand total and then work out what total amount you should each have.

YOU MIGHT LIKE TO: give your child some numbers (always multiples of 3, such as 63 or 99) and see how quickly he or she can divide up each number into two

shares so that one share is twice as much as the other.

IF YOU GET STUCK:
● Make the problem simpler by aiming to divide the numbers into two equal shares (it will still work).
● Use a calculator to do the sums, freeing your child to concentrate on deciding which groups of numbers to try.

Please sign: . . . .

SUM DIGITS

YOU WILL NEED: a helper, a pencil and paper.

YOU ARE GOING TO: use your addition skills to solve this problem.

❑ Can you place each of the digits 1–9 **once only** in the nine circles below to make a correct addition sum?

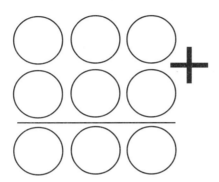

❑ Bring your solution back to school.

BET YOU CAN'T

Do it again – but this time, make sure that no two consecutive digits are next to each other (either side by side or above and below). 1 and 9 count as consecutive.

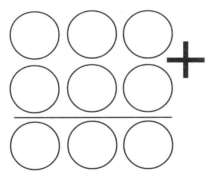

DEAR HELPER

THE POINT OF THIS ACTIVITY: is to practise using mental addition skills. It requires careful thinking about what the digits in each column will add up to. Remember that units or tens carried over will alter column totals.

YOU MIGHT LIKE TO: find several different solutions to the first problem together. How many can you find?

IF YOU GET STUCK:
● Don't worry if you can't find a solution – lots of useful maths will have been done along the way!
● If you spot a solution before your child sees it, give him or her 'clues' by writing in two or three digits in the correct places.

Please sign: . . . .

CRYPTARITHMS

YOU WILL NEED: a helper, a pencil and paper.

YOU ARE GOING TO: use your addition skills to solve a tricky problem!
❑ Can you and your helper solve this unusual sum, called a **cryptarithm**?
Cryptarithms are mathematical problems where digits are represented by letters. Each letter represents a different digit from 0–9. Not every digit is used in this sum, since there are only eight different letters:

```
    O N E
+ F O U R
  F I V E
```

Well, R must be 0 since E stays as just E.

❑ Can you work out which letter represents which digit? There is more than one correct answer.
❑ Bring your solution back to school.

BET YOU CAN'T
Solve this cryptarithm:

```
    I T
+ T O
  T O T
```

Again, each letter represents a different digit from 0–9. Three different digits are needed. This time, there is only one correct answer.

DEAR HELPER

THE POINT OF THIS ACTIVITY: is to practise paper and pencil addition and subtraction methods, while at the same time developing logical thought. Solving this problem need not be guesswork! Start by looking at E and R. What digit must R be if E remains unchanged? Is there only one possible answer for E, or could it be one of several digits?

Get organized: list the digits 0–9 and match letters as you work together.

YOU MIGHT LIKE TO: see how many different solutions you can find to the first problem.

IF YOU GET STUCK: and your child becomes frustrated, make some suggestions. In the first problem, you could try E = 5, O = 2 and F = 1, then let your child work out the rest.

Please sign: . . . .

ALPHABETICAL ARITHMETIC

YOU WILL NEED: a helper, a pencil and paper.

YOU ARE GOING TO: add up some letters to find out what words are worth!
❑ If A = 1, B = 2 and so on, how many words can you and your helper find that total 100 exactly?

Here are clues to some of the words that total 100:

**A reddish-coloured vegetable.
Something your teacher might say when you take this homework back to school!
A piece of equipment you might use with a computer.
A public building that every city needs.
Men with magical powers.**

❑ Can you work these out, and find some more of your own? Maybe your name is worth 100!
❑ Bring all your words back to school to compile a class list.

BET YOU CAN'T
Find any words whose **product** is 100 when the values of the letters are multiplied together.

DEAR HELPER

THE POINT OF THIS ACTIVITY: is to provide a motivating challenge which involves lots of addition and estimation. Work alongside your child, and involve other people if possible.

Start by writing out A–Z with each letter's value clearly recorded. As a warm-up exercise, find the values of your family's names. If any name comes close to 100, this will give you a starting point. One strategy your child may try is to assemble high-value groups of letters (such as 'ex' and 'th'), then try to make words that include them.

YOU MIGHT LIKE TO: collate other groups of words with different total values, such as 10, 99 or 50.

IF YOU GET STUCK:
● Look at the list of letter values again.
● Remind your child to start with the biggest numbers when adding up. For example, in the word HOUSE (8 + 15 + 21 + 19 + 5), start with 21 + 19, then add 15, then add 8 and 5.

Please sign: . . . .

STEP UP

YOU WILL NEED: a helper, a pencil and paper.

YOU ARE GOING TO: use your adding and subtracting skills to solve a problem.
❏ Can you and your helper work out what numbers are missing from this pyramid?

The number in each brick is the sum of the numbers in the two bricks directly beneath it. Both of the missing base numbers are less than 20.

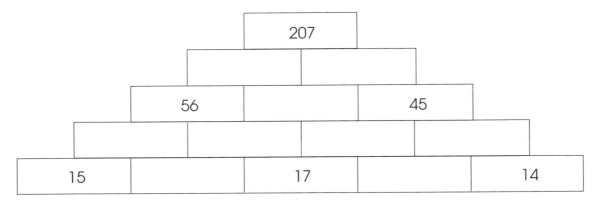

| 207 |
| 56 | 45 |
| 15 | 17 | 14 |

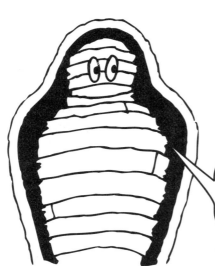

❏ Can you work out a rule for finding a missing base number, if you know the numbers on either side and the number directly above in the third layer?
❏ Bring your completed pyramid and rule for finding the numbers back to school.

BET YOU CAN'T
Invent your own number pyramid puzzle to try out in class.

DEAR HELPER

THE POINT OF THIS ACTIVITY: is to encourage your child to think 'If... then...' and to try out possibilities. This problem involves practising these skills with relatively simple numbers, and is very satisfying to solve! The missing numbers can be found through trial and error – but to find the rule, your child needs to look for the pattern in each mini-pyramid of six numbers.

YOU MIGHT LIKE TO: make up more pyramid puzzles for your child to solve.

IF YOU GET STUCK:
● Work through the problem by trying each number from 1–20 for the missing base numbers, until you find numbers that fit.
● Make up your own simplified pyramid puzzle, using smaller base numbers, to help your child grasp the method.

Please sign: . . . .

IMPACT

ADDITION AND SUBTRACTION

FROM 5S TO 50S

YOU WILL NEED: a helper, a pencil and paper.

YOU ARE GOING TO: extend your times table knowledge.
If you know the 5 times table, then you also know the 50 times table. Here's how!

If 3 × 5 = 15, then 3 × 50 = 150.

As the number 5 gets 10 times bigger, a 0 is added to the answer because the digits move one place to the left and the gap is filled with a 0.

5 × 50 is what?

5 × 5 = 25 so... 250!

❑ Get your helper to ask you some questions about the 50 times table, either spoken or written down.
❑ Come back to school ready for a 50 times table test.

BET YOU CAN'T
❑ Work out how to say the 500 times table – and then the 5000 times table.
❑ Work out how to say the 40 or the 60 times table.

DEAR HELPER

THE POINT OF THIS ACTIVITY: is to help your child to multiply numbers by 10 mentally. This is an important mental maths skill. If children learn and understand the trick of 'adding a 0', a whole new area of mental calculation opens up. Spend as much time on this as you need to, working on paper to illustrate what is happening before your child tries to answer the questions mentally.

YOU MIGHT LIKE TO: try some other '10 times bigger' tables, such as 70 or 30.

IF YOU GET STUCK: write out the 5 times table as a reference, so that your child can see the pattern when he or she says the 50 times table out loud.

Please sign: . . . .

SECRET NUMBERS

YOU WILL NEED: a helper, a pencil and paper.

YOU ARE GOING TO: use your number knowledge to find mystery numbers.

❏ Ask your helper to choose two numbers between 1 and 10 and to call them **a** and **b**, but not tell you what numbers they are. He or she should then write down the **sum** of the two secret numbers in this way:

$$a + b =$$

❏ Try to guess the numbers. Were you right?

❏ If not, ask your helper to write down the **product** of the same two numbers in this way:

$$a \times b =$$

❏ Can you work out what the two numbers are now?

❏ To know which number is **a** and which is **b**, ask what **a + 1** is. Now say what each letter stands for.

❏ Take turns to choose two numbers and play in this way.

❏ Are there any pairs of numbers that you still can't be sure about after having both the sum and product clues?

❏ Bring a pair of secret numbers back to school to try on the class.

BET YOU CAN'T

Make the game harder by having three secret numbers: **a**, **b** and **c**.

DEAR HELPER

THE POINT OF THIS ACTIVITY: is to ensure that your child becomes familiar with the words **sum** and **product** and understands the difference between them. Make sure that you reinforce these key words as you test each other. The activity also involves using letters to stand for numbers, which is an important strategy in mathematical problem-solving.

YOU MIGHT LIKE TO: make up some different clues, such as **2a =** or **2a + b =** or **a − b =**. Which clues are most helpful? Which are least helpful?

IF YOU GET STUCK:

● Choose very small pairs of numbers (both under 5) to start with.

● After the first clue, write out all the possible answers with your child. For example, if **a + b = 5**, the numbers could be 4 and 1 or 1 and 4 or 3 and 2 or 2 and 3. If all these options are written out, it will be easier for your child to see which pair is correct when the product is given.

Please sign: . . . .

MAKING MULTIPLES

YOU WILL NEED: a helper, a pack of cards with all the court cards (Jacks, Queens and Kings) removed.

YOU ARE GOING TO: practise times tables by playing a game.

❑ Shuffle the cards. Decide on a times table you want to practise – maybe the 6 times table.

❑ Deal two cards, laying them down in front of you and your helper.
For example:

❑ If you can use these cards to make a **multiple of 6** in any way (add, subtract, multiply, divide or make a 2-digit number), remove them and start a discard pile.

❑ Now deal two more cards and try again.

❑ If it is impossible, deal one more card. You can use all three cards, or any two of the three.

❑ If you are still stuck, deal another card. Keep going until you can find a way to make a multiple of 6.

❑ Pick up the two (or more) cards that make a multiple of 6 and put them on the discard pile.

❑ Keep playing in this way. Can you use up the whole pack of cards?

❑ Back in school, tell the class about how you played the game.

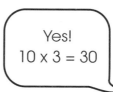

YOU MIGHT LIKE TO TRY

Playing the same game with other times tables. Is it harder with some tables than with others?

DEAR HELPER

THE POINT OF THIS ACTIVITY: is to practise times tables. It also encourages creative thinking with numbers. Help your child to play around with the cards, trying various methods, rather than just waiting for a pair of numbers which multiply to give a number in the 6 times table.

of 6. So 10 + 8 = 18 would be allowed, but 5 + 5 + 8 = 18 would not be.

IF YOU GET STUCK: encourage your child to write out all the multiples in the times table you are working with and use this as a reference.

YOU MIGHT LIKE TO: try playing with two packs of cards, but only allowing two cards to make a multiple

Please sign: . . . .

MULTIPLICATION AND DIVISION

PRODUCT PONTOON

YOU WILL NEED: one or more helpers to play with (three or more is best), a pack of cards with the Court cards (Jack, Queen, King) removed, three counters (buttons or coins) for each player.

YOU ARE GOING TO: play a card game to practise the times tables.
❑ Share out the counters, then deal a card face down to each player.
❑ Each player looks at his or her own card, then puts a counter in the middle.
❑ Now deal a second card to each player.
❑ Each player shows his or her pair of cards and says the product of the two numbers. (Aces count as 11.) The highest product wins all the counters in the middle.

❑ Back in school, tell the class about how your games went – and be ready to play the game again!

BET YOU CAN'T
Play a risk-taking version! After getting two cards, the players can choose either to 'twist' (be given a third card) or 'stick' (stay as they are). If they 'twist', they have to put in another counter. When the extra cards have been dealt, everyone lays their cards on the table and says the product of any **two** of the cards. The highest product wins all the counters in the middle.

DEAR HELPER

THE POINT OF THIS ACTIVITY: is to practise remembering times tables, and to reinforce the use of the word **product**. Try to use this word as often as possible while playing. Before you start, discuss what some of the 'hands' of cards might be. *What would be the best hand? What would be the worst? If you started with a 9 and I started with a 5, what cards would have to be dealt for me to end up winning?*

YOU MIGHT LIKE TO: investigate which products

come up most often, and which come up least often.

IF YOU GET STUCK:
● Have a list of times tables (up to 11 × 11), or a calculator, at hand to check if there is a disagreement.
● Simplify the game by playing with three cards, but for the highest sum rather than the highest product.

Please sign: . . . .

IMPACT

FACTOR GRID

YOU WILL NEED: a helper, a gameboard sheet (page 30), pencils, a dice.

YOU ARE GOING TO: play a dice game to test your knowledge of factors.

❑ Play with the first two grids on the gameboard. Using one grid each, take turns to roll the dice and write the number in one of the squares.

❑ Try to place each number in a square where it is a **factor** of the number on the left-hand side of the row **and** the number at the top of the column. If you cannot do this, try for **either** the correct row **or** the correct column.

❑ Have nine goes each. You must place each number that you roll, even if there is no space in a correct row or column available for it.

❑ When you have both had nine goes, add up your scores. You score one point for each number correctly placed in a row or a column, andtwo points for both. The maximum possible score is 9 × 2 = 18.

❑ Bring your completed grids back to school.

	20	9	36	Score
24				➤
25				➤
18				➤
Score	▼	▼	▼	

YOU MIGHT LIKE TO TRY

Writing some grid numbers in the blank gameboards to make your own game, then playing it.

DEAR HELPER

THE POINT OF THIS ACTIVITY: is to practise times tables – and, in particular, knowledge of **factors**. Factors are numbers which go into other numbers a whole number of times (for example, 4 goes into 12 three times, so 4 and 3 are factors of 12).

Before you start, discuss what will be the best number to roll (1, since it goes into any number). There is a lot of strategic thinking involved – for example, 1 is the only **common factor** of 9 and 25, so don't waste a roll of 1 on a square where other factors are shared.

Talk about your child's decisions: *Well, you could put a 4 there, because it is a factor of 20. But is 4 a factor of*

18? What about 25? What about 24? So where should you put it?

YOU MIGHT LIKE TO: ask your child to make up a grid that would allow you to score 18 if you rolled 4, 5 and 6 three times each. All the grid numbers must be different!

IF YOU GET STUCK: keep a set of times tables handy for reference.

Please sign: . . . .

MULTIPLICATION AND DIVISION

IMPACT

FACTOR GRID BOARDS

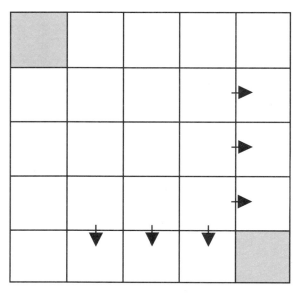

	20	9	36	Score
24				▶
25				▶
18				▶
Score	▼	▼	▼	

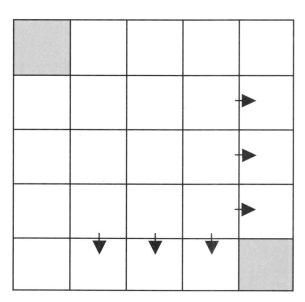

	20	9	36	Score
24				▶
25				▶
18				▶
Score	▼	▼	▼	

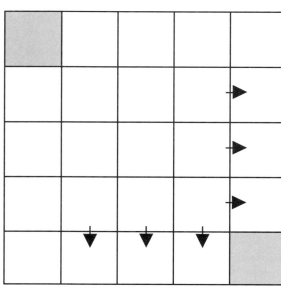

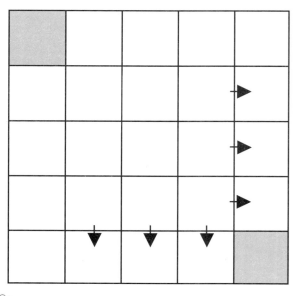

MULTIPLICATION AND DIVISION

IMPACT

MENTAL MATHS HOMEWORK

SORT THE SWEETS

YOU WILL NEED: a helper, a paper and pencils.

YOU ARE GOING TO: use your knowledge of times tables to solve a problem.
❑ Can you and your helper solve this problem?

The number of sweets in a pile is **less than 100**.
If they are divided into piles of 5, there is 1 left over.
If they are divided into piles of 9, there are 4 left over.
If they are divided into piles of 4, there are none left over.
What is the **largest** possible number of sweets in this pile?

❑ Bring your solution back to school.

BET YOU CAN'T
Find a number **over** 100 that gives the same results when divided in the same ways as above.

DEAR HELPER

THE POINT OF THIS ACTIVITY: is to practise knowledge of the pattern of times tables. Start by discussing with your child what he or she can tell about the mystery number from the clues given – for example, if it is one more than a multiple of 5, it must end with a 1 or a 6. Once you have narrowed down the field, look for the highest number that meets all the criteria.

YOU MIGHT LIKE TO: ask your child to write a similar problem for you (and your child's friends) to try.

IF YOU GET STUCK: write out the 5 times table (up to 100), then write a new column alongside it with 1 added to each number. Write out the 9 times table (up to 99), then write out a new column with 4 added to each number. Write out the 4 times table (up to 100). Look for the highest common number in the three appropriate columns.

Please sign: . . . .

MENTAL MATHS HOMEWORK

MULTIPLICATION AND DIVISION *(vertical text, left margin)*

GET SET, GO!

YOU WILL NEED: a helper, paper and pencils, a pack of playing cards with the court cards (Jacks, Queens, Kings) taken out, the 'Sets' sheet (page 33).

YOU ARE GOING TO: use times table knowledge to sort some numbers into sets.

❑ Look at the first diagram on the 'Sets' sheet. Label one set '3', one '4' and one '5'.

❑ Shuffle the cards and divide them into two equal piles.

❑ Take turns with your helper to turn over the top card from each pile and find the **product** of the two numbers.

❑ Write your answer on the sets diagram **in the right place**. To go in a set, the number must be a **multiple** of the set number. If the number is not a multiple of 3, 4 or 5, it must be written outside the three circles.

❑ How many numbers have been written inside the circles by the time you have turned over all the cards?

Here is an example of a game being played:

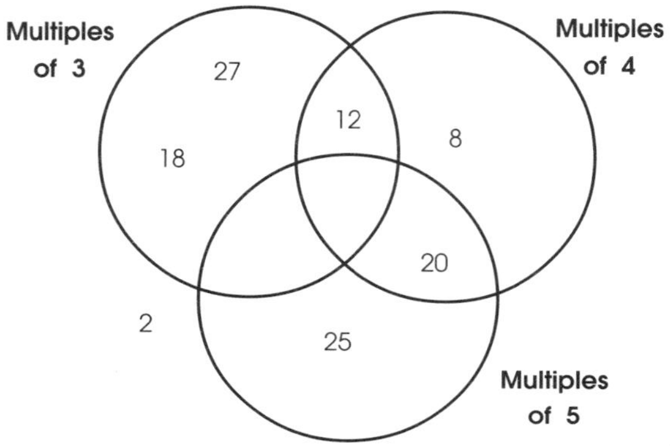

Multiples of 3   27   Multiples of 4

18   12   8

20

2   25

Multiples of 5

8 × 5 = 40
That's a multiple of 4 **and** 5.

❑ Bring your completed diagram back to school.

BET YOU CAN'T:

Play again, using the other 'Sets' diagram with three new set numbers.

DEAR HELPER

THE POINT OF THIS ACTIVITY: is to practise times tables to 10 × 10. It also requires your child to know multiples of 3, 4 and 5 beyond the familar times tables.

A key element in this activity is realizing that some numbers rolled belong in overlapping areas: they are multiples of 3 **and** 4, of 3 **and** 5 or of 4 **and** 5. Talk about this, and encourage your child to predict numbers that would belong in particular spaces on the diagram: *What numbers would belong in the very centre?* (Multiples of 3, 4 **and** 5.)

YOU MIGHT LIKE TO: ask your child to find three set

numbers that would mean that very few numbers can be placed in the overlapping set areas.

IF YOU GET STUCK:

● Start with the set numbers 2, 5 and 10, as the multiples of these numbers are easy to recognize. What can your child say about all the numbers in the very centre?

● Use a dice to make the numbers instead of cards, so that the products are smaller.

Please sign: . . . .

IMPACT *(vertical text, left margin)*

MENTAL MATHS HOMEWORK

SETS

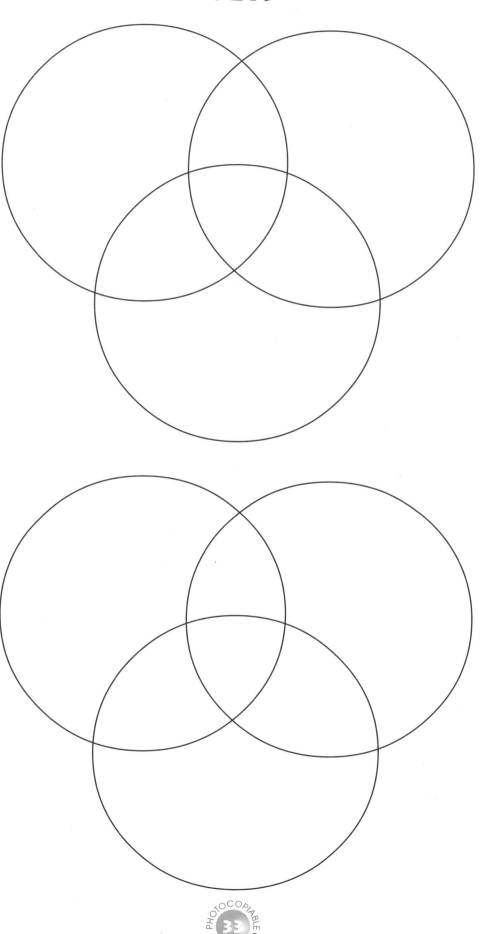

PERSISTENT NUMBERS

YOU WILL NEED: a helper, a pencil and paper.

YOU ARE GOING TO: investigate a number pattern, using times table knowledge. The **persistence** of a number is given by the number of steps it takes to reach a single digit when the digits of the number are multiplied together. For example:

$$86 \rightarrow 8 \times 6 = 48 \rightarrow \qquad 4 \times 8 = 32 \rightarrow \qquad 3 \times 2 = 6$$
$$\text{1 step} \qquad\qquad\qquad \text{2 steps} \qquad\qquad \text{3 steps}$$

so 78 has a persistence of 3.

❑ Can you and your helper find the **smallest** number which has a persistence of 2, and the **smallest** number which has a persistence of 3? Both numbers are under 50.

❑ Bring your answers back to school.

BET YOU CAN'T
Find the smallest number with a persistence of 4. It is over 50.

DEAR HELPER

THE POINT OF THIS ACTIVITY: is to practise times tables, and to develop problem-solving techniques. Start by drawing up a chart to find the persistence of each number from 10 to 50 (as above), so that you start off by working in a systematic way. Encourage your child to talk about the numbers and to predict what each number's persistence will be.

YOU MIGHT LIKE TO: ask your child to explain what kind of number will have a persistence of 1.

IF YOU GET STUCK: work through methodically from 10, and you will begin to see a pattern.

Please sign: . . . .

Multiplication and Division — IMPACT

MYSTERY SYMBOLS

YOU WILL NEED: a helper, a pencil and paper.

YOU ARE GOING TO: use your number skills to solve a very tricky problem!
❑ Can you and your helper work out the value of the three mystery symbols in this grid?

♣	♦	♥	♦	**17**
♣	♥	♣	♥	
♥	♦	♥	♦	
♦	♣	♦	♣	**20**

19

❑ Can you now work out the missing totals of the rows and columns?
❑ Bring your solution back to school.

BET YOU CAN'T
Make up a similar puzzle of your own to bring back to school.

DEAR HELPER

THE POINT OF THIS ACTIVITY: is to help your child with the work on algebra that he or she is doing in school. Working out the number value of symbols from information given is an important part of algebra.

Look for a good place to start on the puzzle. Work out what would **not** be a sensible guess for a symbol ('Well, heart can't equal as much as 20'). Have a guess ('Let's try heart = 9, diamond = 4 and clubs = 5'), and work through some rows and columns. Look out for relationships which will make it easier to spot the answers.

YOU MIGHT LIKE TO: help your child to invent a similar puzzle by working backwards. Give three symbols a value each, draw them in a blank grid, then give a few totals of rows and columns.

IF YOU GET STUCK: start with the bottom row. If two clubs and two diamonds make 20, one club and one diamond make 10.

Please sign: . . . .

MYSTERY SQUARES

YOU WILL NEED: a helper, a pencil and paper.

❑ On the addition and multiplication grids below, the outside numbers (the numbers you have to add or multiply) are missing. Can you work out what they should be?

The missing outside numbers on each grid are 1, 2, 3, 4, 5, 6, 7, 8, 9 and 10. Each number is used once only.

+					
		9	4		12
	14			9	
			3		
	17				16

×					
		30			
			24	36	
		20		18	
	40				8

❑ Bring your answers back to school.

BET YOU CAN'T
Solve both grids in 10 minutes.

DEAR HELPER

THE POINT OF THIS ACTIVITY: is to practise remembering the number bonds (additions) and times tables for the numbers 1 to 10. Knowing these number facts is important, and these puzzles test your child's knowledge in a fun and challenging way which also requires some logical thinking.

The addition square rehearses the logic needed to tackle the harder multiplication square. For each square, there are choices to be made: 'The 12 could be 4 + 8, but then I can't make 16, so I'll try 3 + 9...' and so on.

YOU MIGHT LIKE TO: make up another mystery square for your child to solve.

IF YOU GET STUCK:
● Start by trying to make the 3 in the addition square and the 20 in the multiplication square. Once you have sorted out where to start, the rest becomes easier.
● Remind your child that no number can be added to or multiplied by itself.

Please sign: . . . .

MULTIPLICATION AND DIVISION

IMPACT

BUTTONS IN A JAR

YOU WILL NEED: a helper, a pencil and paper.

YOU ARE GOING TO: use logic to solve a button problem.
❑ Can you and your helper solve this problem?

In a jar, there are 36 buttons. There are twice as many whites as greens, one less blues than greens, and seven more reds than greens. How many buttons of each colour are in the jar?

❑ Bring your solution back to school.

BET YOU CAN'T
Make up a similar problem with your helper, and bring it back to school to test the class! Choose a total number of buttons less than 100, and use four different colours of buttons.

DEAR HELPER

THE POINT OF THIS ACTIVITY: is to develop problem-solving techniques, particularly skills of 'sensible guessing' and trial and error. Before you start, establish what would be a 'silly' guess (for example, 50 green buttons), and why. Once you have a sensible guess for green, such as 20, organize your tries systematically. You will soon reach the answer!

YOU MIGHT LIKE TO: set your child a 'real' problem

by putting some different kinds of buttons or assorted small objects into a bag, then giving your child clues about the numbers.

IF YOU GET STUCK: the key colour to find first is green, since all the other colour clues link to green. Work systematically, trying 1 green, then 2 green and so on.

Please sign: . . . .

MENTAL MATHS HOMEWORK

3-WAY BINGO

YOU WILL NEED: a helper, the 'Bingo cards' sheet, about 40 counters (buttons or 1p coins would do), two dice.

YOU ARE GOING TO: play Bingo!

❏ Cut out the two Bingo cards and take one each.

❏ Take turns to roll the two dice. On your turn, if you can find a number on your card that is either the **sum of**, the **product of** or the **difference between** the two numbers you have rolled, cover this on your card.

❏ The winner is the first player to cover all the numbers on his or her card.

❏ Bring back to school your thoughts about which numbers were the hardest to cover. Why do you think they were the hardest?

BET YOU CAN'T

Set a time limit and see how many numbers you can cover in that time. Think fast!

DEAR HELPER

THE POINT OF THIS ACTIVITY: is to practise quick recall of number facts. It also encourages strategic thinking about which numbers to choose. A good strategy is to make the more 'difficult' numbers whenever possible.

This game also provides an opportunity to reinforce the words **sum**, **product** and **difference**. Try to use these words on each turn, talking through the three options: *You've rolled 2 and 4. The **sum** of 2 and 4 is... and the **product** is... and the **difference** between them is... Which will you cover?*

YOU MIGHT LIKE TO: make the game move faster by saying that you win if you cover a vertical line of four numbers.

IF YOU GET STUCK: write out all the numbers that could be made with each roll as you go along. These will provide a reference if the same pair of numbers comes up again.

Please sign: . . . .

3-WAY BINGO GAMEBOARDS

0 / 1	2	3	4	5
6	7	8	9	10
11	12	15	16	18
20	24	25	30	36

0 / 1	2	3	4	5
6	7	8	9	10
11	12	15	16	18
20	24	25	30	36

MENTAL MATHS HOMEWORK

DOUBLE-AGE PAIRS

YOU WILL NEED: a helper, a pencil and paper.

YOU ARE GOING TO: investigate the ages of your family.

❑ With your helper, try to answer these questions:

Are you **twice as old** as anyone in your family? If not, were you ever? Will you ever be?

Are you **half as old** as anyone in your family? If not, were you ever? Will you ever be?

❑ Record your answers like this:

In _____, when I was/will be _____, I will be half as old/twice as

old as my _____, who will be _____ .

❑ Bring your answers back to school.

BET YOU CAN'T

Say what is special about the age you will be when you are **half** as old as your helper.

DEAR HELPER

THE POINT OF THIS ACTIVITY: is to practise doubling and halving numbers mentally, as well as to develop logical thinking and problem-solving skills. For one year in most of our lives, we will be half as old as each of our parents. Even siblings now aged 10 and 12 were, years ago, a 'double-age pair'. Encourage your child to talk out loud as he or she tries to explain how this works.

YOU MIGHT LIKE TO: ask your child to think about whether there can be 'triple-age pairs' – that is, a family member who is **three times** the child's age. Will this occur before or after the double-age pair?

IF YOU GET STUCK: try to be methodical. Start with you and your child. Keep adding 1 to each of your ages until you reach a double-age pair. Repeat for other family members, writing each person's age in a separate column.

Please sign: . . . .

MYSTERY NUMBER SEARCH 1

YOU WILL NEED: a helper, a pencil and paper.

YOU ARE GOING TO: investigate some special numbers.
There is a number under 100 that has this special property:

Add 1 to it, and the result is a square number. Halve it and then add 1, and the result is also a square number.

❏ What is the number?

> Try 26.
> 26 plus 1 is 27. That is not a square number.
> Half of 26 is 13, plus 1 is 14. That isn't either.

> Try 63.
> 63 plus 1 is 64. That **is** a square number!
> But half of 63... oh, 31.5, plus 1 is 32.5. That certainly isn't!

❏ Bring your answer back to school.

BET YOU CAN'T

Find the next number with the same property.

DEAR HELPER

THE POINT OF THIS ACTIVITY: is to develop problem-solving skills. It also requires a working knowledge of square numbers. By Year 5, your child will need to be familiar with **square numbers** (numbers formed by multiplying a whole number by itself) and to know the sequence of square numbers to 100.

Encourage your child to work systematically, and to record his or her investigation in an ordered and logical way.

YOU MIGHT LIKE TO: create some mystery number puzzles of your own to try on each other.

IF YOU GET STUCK: write out all the square numbers to 100 (10 × 10). Look at all the numbers that are one less, starting with the smallest: 3, 8, 15 and so on.

Please sign: . . . .

NAME

DATE

MYSTERY NUMBER SEARCH 2

YOU WILL NEED: a helper, a pencil and paper.

YOU ARE GOING TO: search for a special number.
❏ Can you and your helper solve this puzzle?

What is the number under 30 for which the digits are reversed when you double it and add 2?

❏ You and your helper will need to be well organized and systematic to solve this. Try testing numbers in this way:

Number	Double it	Add 2	Right number?
10	2 × 10 = 20	20 + 2 = 22	No
11	2 × 11 = 22	22 + 2 = 24	No

❏ Bring your answer back to school.

BET YOU CAN'T
Find the next highest number for which this is true.

DEAR HELPER

THE POINT OF THIS ACTIVITY: is to encourage your child to be able to apply his or her mathematical knowledge and to develop skills to help tackle problems successfully. Read through the problem slowly and choose a number to try step by step.
  Encourage your child to work systematically, and to record his or her investigation in an ordered and logical way.

YOU MIGHT LIKE TO: create some similar problems together, for your child to take back to school. Make sure they can be solved!

IF YOU GET STUCK: be reassured, you will reach the answer quite quickly if you work methodically!

Please sign: . . . .

Sidebar: MULTISTEP AND MIXED OPERATIONS / IMPACT

MONEY PROBLEM

YOU WILL NEED: a helper, pencil and paper.

YOU ARE GOING TO: Use all your number knowledge to solve a problem.

❏ Can you and your helper solve this problem? You will need to be logical and think carefully.

A bag of money has 22 coins in it.
The bag contains only 10p, 5p and 1p coins.
If the total amount of money is £1.50, how many of each coin are in the bag?

❏ Bring your answer back to school.

BET YOU CAN'T

Work out what is the **greatest** amount of money the bag could contain if it had 20 coins in it (only 10p, 5p and 1p coins, and at least **one** of each).

DEAR HELPER

THE POINT OF THIS ACTIVITY: is to to apply mathematical knowledge and to develop problem-solving skills. Read through the problem slowly. Help your child to be organized and systematic in his or her working, and check for each try whether the two conditions (there are 22 coins **and** a total of £1.50) have been met.

YOU MIGHT LIKE TO: make up a similar problem together for your child to take back to school.

IF YOU GET STUCK:
● Use toy money (or real money), if you have enough, to try different combinations of coins.
● Don't worry if you don't find the answer – this problem is a real challenge! Help your child to enjoy the process of working, and be encouraging when he or she comes close to the answer.

Please sign: . . . .

MENTAL MATHS HOMEWORK

NUMBER CRUNCH

YOU WILL NEED: a helper, three dice, paper, a pencil each, colouring pencils.

YOU ARE GOING TO: play a dice game that tests your number skills.

❑ Take turns to roll the three dice and write down the three numbers rolled (for example: 2, 4 and 4).

❑ Create number sentences to make as many different numbers as possible using the three numbers you have rolled. Write down the number sentences and record the numbers made. You must follow these rules:

1. Each number sentence must contain the three dice numbers **once only**.

2. You may put two dice numbers together to create two-digit numbers.

3. You may include decimals and negative numbers.

❑ When you have made all the numbers you can, roll the dice again to get three new dice numbers.

❑ After three rolls of the dice, whoever has made more numbers is the winner.

❑ Bring your number sentences back to school.

YOU MIGHT LIKE TO TRY
Changing the rules so that only one roll of the three dice is allowed, and a time limit is set.

$$2 \times 4 \times 4 = 32$$
$$2 \times 4 + 4 = 12$$
$$2 \times (4+4) = 16$$
$$24 + 4 = 28$$
$$2 - 4 - 4 = -6$$
$$44 + 2 = 46$$

MULTISTEP AND MIXED OPERATIONS

IMPACT

DEAR HELPER

THE POINT OF THIS ACTIVITY: is to apply a range of number skills to a game.

Encourage your child to be as creative as possible: do not allow him or her to give up and re-roll the dice before all the possible answers are found.

Make sure that the numbers rolled are recorded as well as the number sentences, in case there is any disagreement!

YOU MIGHT LIKE TO: discuss with your child which groups of three numbers are 'good' to roll, and which are of limited use.

IF YOU GET STUCK: work together with your child to make as many numbers as possible.

Please sign: . . . .

HOW MANY 5S?

YOU WILL NEED: a helper, a pencil and paper.

YOU ARE GOING TO: solve a problem that is all about 5s.
❏ Can you and your helper answer these questions?

**555 digits are used to number all the pages in a book.
How many pages are there in the book?
How many times is the digit 5 used?**

❏ Write down your solution, and show the method you have used to work it out.
❏ Bring your solution back to school, and be ready to explain it.

BET YOU CAN'T

Turn the problem around and work out how many digits are needed for the page numbers in a book with 555 pages.

DEAR HELPER

THE POINT OF THIS ACTIVITY: is to help your child with the problem solving work that he or she is doing in school. This problem could be solved by simply writing out the numbers and keeping a count of digits – but there must be a quicker way! Help your child to think and talk about how you might speed things up. *How many digits are needed for pages 1–10? How many for pages 11–20, and then 21–30, and so on? What about 101–110?* Mental calculation skills of adding and multiplying will be needed.

YOU MIGHT LIKE TO: choose a reading book and

help your child to work out how many digits have been used to number the pages.

IF YOU GET STUCK:
● Use a calculator for adding up, so that your child's energy goes into solving the problem.
● Simplify the problem by working out how many pages (and how many 5s) are needed if only 55 digits are used.

Please sign: . . . .

KEEP FIT CALCULATIONS

YOU WILL NEED: a helper, a pencil and paper.

YOU ARE GOING TO: exercise your mind with a number problem!
❏ Can you and your helper answer this question?

Jo is training for Sports Day. Each day, she runs round and round the playground. At the end of seven days, she has completed 182 circuits in all. Each day, she did six more circuits than the day before. How many circuits did she complete on the first day?

❏ Choose a number to try. Lay out your work like this:

Try 1:	20 circuits	
Day 1		20
Day 2	+ 6 =	26
Day 3	+ 6 =	32
Day 4	+ 6 =	38
Day 5	+ 6 =	44
Day 6	+ 6 =	50
Day 7	+ 6 =	56
Total		266

Too many.
Try 15 next.

❏ Bring your solution back to school.

BET YOU CAN'T

Work out how many circuits Jo did on the first day of the following week, when her total went up to 210.

DEAR HELPER

THE POINT OF THIS ACTIVITY: is to improve your child's problem-solving techniques. This problem requires estimation and addition. It can be solved through trial and error, using a logical approach. When you start, organize your work as shown above. Help your child to make reasonable guesses based on the results that he or she finds, and to narrow down the field of options. You need a total with 2 in the units column, so encourage your child to look ahead as the adding up is done.

YOU MIGHT LIKE TO: Work with your child to make

up another problem for him or her to try out in class.

IF YOU GET STUCK:
● A useful strategy for adding up columns of numbers like this is to look for pairs of digits that total 10 in a column and add them first.
● If your child struggles with the calculation, use a calculator so that his or her energies can go into making sensible guesses to solve the problem.

Please sign: . . . .

MOUTH-WATERING MATHS

YOU WILL NEED: a helper, a cookery book or magazine with recipes (using metric weights), a pencil and paper.

YOU ARE GOING TO: do some cooking in your head!

❑ Choose a simple recipe – a cake or soup recipe will do.

❑ Write down the ingredients and how much of each you need. Don't write out how to do the recipe.

❑ Underneath, write the same list again – but this time, **halve** the quantities. Even if some of the new quantities are strange (like half an egg), write them down.

❑ Now write out the recipe again – but this time, work out what you would need to make **ten times** the original amount (for a big party).

❑ Bring your new ingredients lists back to school.

BET YOU CAN'T

Work out what quantities you would need for three or four times the original amount.

DEAR HELPER

THE POINT OF THIS ACTIVITY: is to help your child become familiar with using metric measures and doing practical calculations. Halving, doubling and multiplying by 10 are important mental skills. To multiply a number by 10, all you have to do is move the digits of the number one place to the left: 40 becomes 400, 500 becomes 5000, and so on.

Where possible, encourage your child to convert weights in grams to kilograms and grams. 1000 grams (1000g) = 1 kilogram (1kg).

YOU MIGHT LIKE TO: practise converting weights from g to kg and vice versa (for example, 0.62 kg = 620g).

IF YOU GET STUCK: look through the recipes first and try to choose one with simple weights (such as 50g or 200g) that will be easy to halve.

Please sign: . . . .

Dear Parent

We all know that parents are a crucial factor in their children's learning. You can make a huge difference to your child's education. We are planning to send home some activities that fit in with the maths we are doing in school. The activities are designed for your child to do with you, or another available adult. You do not need to know a lot of maths in order to help your child.

These are not traditional homework activities. It is important that your child first explains the activity to you. Each activity will have been explained thoroughly in school. Then do the activity together. By sharing these activities with your child, you will be helping to develop her or his mental maths. And as a result of being given that all-important attention, your child is more likely to become confident and skilled in maths.

We hope, too, that these activities will be fun to do – it matters that children develop positive attitudes to maths. If you are particularly nervous about maths, try not to make your child nervous too! If your child is having difficulties, look at the 'If you get stuck' suggestions which are provided on each activity sheet.

After completing each activity, your child will usually have something to bring back to school. However, sometimes there may not be anything written down to bring back – your child is doing mental maths, so all the work may be in your heads!

If you have any problems with or further questions about any of the activities – or about any of the maths being covered – please do let us know at school. We do very much value your support.

Yours sincerely

MENTAL MATHS HOMEWORK